Butterflies

Colouring & Gu

This colouring book includes a few of the more popular butterflies and moths that can be found in Ireland throughout the year. Colouring each one and reading the short descriptions will help you identify some of the more common species. The introduction to this book will also help you understand more about these beautiful insects.

Sometimes the male and female are different colours so we have indicated which one we have included for each species. We have shown you the upper surface of each butterfly or moth as it can be seen when it is flying. When they are resting their wings are often closed, hiding much of the colour. We have also included the English, Latin (scientific name) and Irish name where possible.

Contents

Text & Drawings: Audrey Murphy   *Design & Layout:* Susan Murphy Wickens
With thanks to David Nash, Deirdre Hardiman, Fidelma Ní Ghallchobhair, An Gúm,
Julian Wyllie and Christopher Barry.
Produced by Sherkin Island Marine Station © 2005
ISBN:1 870492 92 7

Further reading:
Collins Wild Guide: Butterflies & Moths of Britain and Europe ISBN: 0-00-220010-4
Field Guide to the Moths of Great Britain and Ireland ISBN: 0-9531399-2-1
The Millennium Atlas of Butterflies in Britain & Ireland ISBN: 0-19-850565-5

This book is sponsored by Cork County Council and the Department of the Environment, Heritage & Local Government through the Environmental Partnership Fund.

Printed on recycled paper

The Study of Butterflies and Moths

There are approximately 156,000 different types of butterflies and moths in the world. Roughly 20,000 of these are butterflies and the rest are moths. Most species never move far from the plant on which they feed, while a few species have travelled a huge distance to Ireland from other countries.

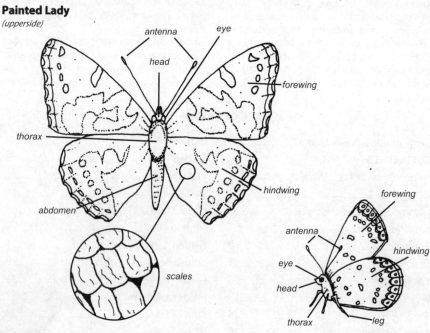

Painted Lady
(upperside)

antenna

eye

head

forewing

thorax

hindwing

abdomen

scales

Common Blue
(underside)

forewing

antenna

hindwing

eye

head

thorax

leg

Butterflies and moths are insects. They are closely related and often look very similar but can vary in size from very small to a size similar to that of a small bird. Their body is divided up into three parts: the head, thorax and abdomen. The head has two antennae, two eyes and a long tube-like tongue called a proboscis, which is coiled up when not in use and opens up for feeding. Most adult butterflies and moths feed on nectar, honeydew or sap. The middle section of the body, the thorax, has four wings and six legs. Each wing is covered in tiny powdery scales, which are arranged in rows like slates on a roof and each scale is a single colour which helps make up unique displays or patterns on the wings. The last section of the body, the abdomen, has no legs or wings.

DIFFERENCE BETWEEN A BUTTERFLY AND A MOTH

There are some ways to tell a butterfly from a moth but there are always exceptions.

Butterflies are usually seen during the day whereas moths are more often seen at night. Moths generally rest during the day and tend to have dull colours to hide them in daylight hours. Some moths however, do come out during the day and are often mistaken for butterflies as they can be just as colourful.

Butterflies tend to fold their wings vertically above themselves when resting whereas moths tend to keep their wings flat and tucked into their body. There are some moths though that, when resting, will hold their wings vertically like butterflies.

Most butterflies have the same type of antennae (also known as feelers) – long and straight with a little 'bubble' or 'club' at the end. The antennae of moths are sometimes feather-like and generally do not have a 'bubble' or 'club' at the end.

THE LIFE CYCLE

A butterfly or moth has four stages in its life cycle: adult, egg, caterpillar and pupa. Some butterflies and moths complete the life cycle once, twice or three times per year. Others may take two years or longer.
Metamorphosis is the complete change that a butterfly or moth goes through to become an adult.

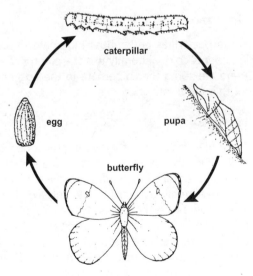

Life cycle of a butterfly

The Egg

The female will lay a tiny egg on the leaf of a plant. Inside the egg, the embryo is forming into a caterpillar (also called a larvae). Soon this caterpillar will hatch out and eat the leaf it is sitting on.

The Caterpillar

The caterpillar that emerges from the egg is soft,  has no wings and looks nothing like the adult butterfly or moth. It has three pairs of legs on the thorax and many false legs on the abdomen. It grows very quickly as it eats a lot of leaves, flowers or fruits, shedding its skin many times to allow it get bigger.

The Pupa

In order to finish the process of turning into a butterfly the caterpillar attaches itself to a firm surface, such as a rock, a branch or the wall of a house. It changes to the pupa stage (also known as the chrysalis), by forming a hard outer skin inside which the caterpillar turns into an adult butterfly or moth.

The Adult

Once the adult is fully formed inside the pupa it breaks 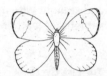 open the hard shell, rests for a few minutes to allow the blood to circulate in its wings and then flies away. Adults live from a few days to some months.

HIBERNATION

Some butterflies and moths hibernate during the winter, sleeping while the weather is cold. Generally it is the caterpillar or pupa stages that hibernate but there are some that hibernate in the egg or adult stages. Each butterfly and moth is different.

PROTECTION

Butterflies, moths and their young must be very careful to avoid being eaten by birds and other predators and so use camouflage to help them blend in with their surroundings. Though butterflies mostly have colourful wings, they may close them while at rest, showing only a dull colour underneath. This makes them less visible to predators. Moths on the other hand keep their wings flat while resting and so have dull colours on the upperside of their wings.

Some butterflies and moths are poisonous, both in the caterpillar and adult stages, and use bright colours to warn off predators. When a young predator tastes one of these and discovers the foul taste, it remembers the bright colours and never eats it again! Some caterpillars have hairs or spines to keep enemies away and others make a tent to hide under for protection. Some caterpillars even have ants to protect them!

WHERE TO LOOK!

For the species that we have included in this book, we have mentioned on which plants the caterpillars or adults like to feed. If you can find these plants you may find some butterflies or moths nearby. Your garden at home or a nearby park are good places to begin your search. Butterflies tend to fly during the day, while moths usually prefer flying at night. Open areas in woodlands on a sunny day are perfect for looking for butterflies and are also good at night to find moths. Moths are often attracted to light so pay particular attention to street lamps or outside lights at your home.

Large White/Cabbage White

Pieris brassicae

Bánóg mhór

The eggs of the Large White (also known as Cabbage White) are laid on the underside of leaves, with caterpillars hatching from these eggs after approximately seven days. The caterpillars cause a lot of damage to cabbage as they feed on its leaves and are also poisonous to predators because of mustard oil in their bodies. The female butterfly is much larger than the male and has two black spots on the upperside of the forewings. The male only has one spot but both male and female have two spots on the underside of the forewings. The Large White is very similar to, but much larger than, the Green-veined White (which has greenish veins on its wings) and to the Small White (which is much smaller than the Large White).

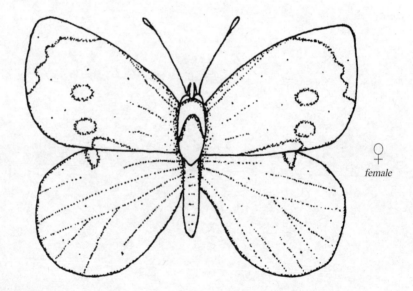

♀
female

BUTTERFLY
Wingspan: 6.4 – 7.6 cm
Colour: White with black tips on the forewings; underwings pale greyish green
Diet: Caterpillars feed on the leaves of cabbages, oil-seed rape and nasturtium flowers.

Winter Hibernating stage: Pupa.
Caterpillar: Green with black spots and a yellow line down the back and sides.
Habitat: Gardens, fields, hedgerows and other flowery places.
Flight Season: April to October.

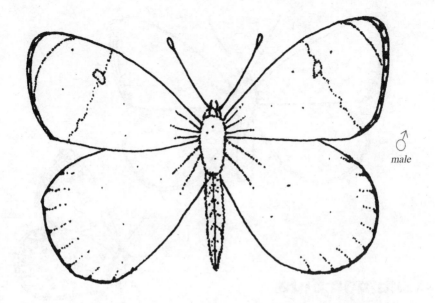

male ♂

Orange Tip

Anthocharis cardamines

Barr buí

The Orange Tip is very common in Ireland and can be seen flying from flower to flower. The female butterfly lays only one egg per plant so as not to draw attention to them. The eggs are laid at the base of flower heads. It is thought that the female leaves a scent behind with the egg so that other female butterflies will know not to lay an egg on the same flower.

BUTTERFLY
Wingspan: 3.8 – 4.8cm
Colour: Forewings white with black tips; large orange patch on the male's forewings; underside speckled black and yellow.
Diet: Adult feeds on nectar of lady's smock and garlic mustard.
Winter Hibernating stage: Pupa.
Caterpillar: Green on top and darker underneath with a white line along each side. Covered in black hairs.
Habitat: Damp areas in woodlands, hedgerows, roadsides, flowery meadows and gardens.
Flight Season: April to June.

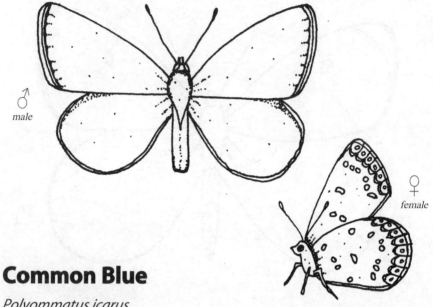

male

♀ *female*

Common Blue

Polyommatus icarus

Gormán coiteann

There are a number of blue butterflies but as the name suggests this is the most common. Although the male is blue the female is actually dark brown with violet blue at the base of the wings. At the edge of the wings are orange crescent shapes. The eggs are laid singly by the female and the caterpillars hatch out after nine days. These caterpillars have a honey gland on their bodies, to which ants are attracted and on which they feed. In return for the honey the ants often provide food, shelter and protection from predators for the caterpillar.

BUTTERFLY
Wingspan: 2.5 – 3cm
Colour: Male violet blue with a fine black line around the edges; underside brownish/grey with black, white and red spots.
Diet: Caterpillar feeds on clover and bird's-foot-trefoil.
Winter Hibernating stage: Caterpillar.
Caterpillar: Green with a darker line down its back and yellow stripes along its sides.
Habitat: Grasslands, gardens, meadows, coastal regions, heaths.
Flight Season: May to September.

Small Tortoiseshell

Aglais urticae

Ruán beag

The Small Tortoiseshell can often be seen flying near windows and the eaves of houses looking for a suitable place to hibernate for the winter. It can be found indoors in the winter if a warm spell wakes it from hibernation. Approximately 1000 eggs are laid in small clusters on the underneath of leaves, which hatch into caterpillars after nine days. For protection these usually live in groups when they are young, but as they get older will move away from the others in order to feed. The Small Tortoiseshell is one of the first butterflies to be seen in spring.

BUTTERFLY

Wingspan: 4.5 – 5cm

Colour: Base colour orange-red with black markings; edges have a row of blue crescents; underside almost black.

Diet: Caterpillar feeds on nettles and the butterfly feeds on the nectar of *Buddleia* (butterfly bush) flowers.

Winter Hibernating stage: Adult butterfly.

Caterpillar: Blackish brown and hairy.

Habitat: In gardens and most flowery places.

Flight Season: March to October.

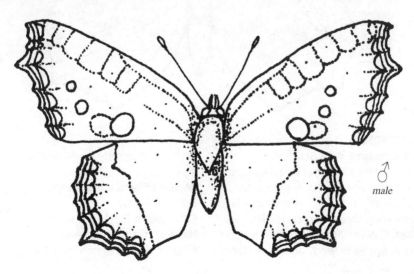

♂
male

Peacock

Inachis io

Péacóg

The Peacock is easy to identify by the four 'peacock eyes' on the upperside of its wings. It has very similar habits to the Small Tortoiseshell in that the adult butterfly enters houses looking for a suitable spot to hibernate for the winter. It can sometimes be found hibernating in tree trunks and piles of wood. The underside is darker in both species enabling them to hide in dark corners during hibernation. The eggs are laid in large groups or clusters on the underside of nettle leaves and hatch after 7–12 days. The new caterpillars will stay in a group until old enough to wander off on their own. The caterpillar can move quickly and if disturbed will raise the front of its body off the ground and form a hook shape. If it gets annoyed it will drop to the ground and wriggle like crazy!

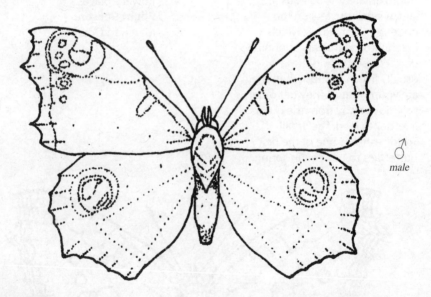

♂
male

BUTTERFLY

Wingspan: 5.4 – 5.8cm
Female slightly larger than the male.
Colour: Dark reddish brown with yellow and black markings; large lilac-blue spot, like an eye, on each wing.
Diet: Caterpillar feeds on nettles and adult butterfly feeds on the nectar of *Buddleia* (butterfly bush) and other flowers.

Winter Hibernating stage: Adult butterfly.
Caterpillar: Black and spiny.
Habitat: Gardens and parks.
Flight Season: March to October.

Red Admiral

Vanessa atalanta

Aimiréal dearg

This butterfly actually lives in the Mediterranean but migrates northwards every year and is therefore called a migrant species. It lays one egg at a time on stinging nettle leaves, allowing it to spread the eggs over large distances. The caterpillar hatches after about a week by biting a hole in the top of the egg. It then lives on its own, wrapped up in a leaf whose edges have been held together by silk which it has spun itself. It gradually eats this shelter and then moves to another leaf where it will make a new shelter.

BUTTERFLY

Wingspan: 6.7 – 7.2cm

Colour: Velvety black/dark brown with red bands and white spots; underside dark brown with orange, blue and white markings.

Diet: Caterpillars feed on nettles, butterflies feed on flower nectar and rotten fruit.

Winter Hibernating stage: Adult butterfly (it rarely survives the cold winters in the north and so is believed to migrate south again in the autumn).

Caterpillar: Brown/black with a yellow stripe along the side and bristles.

Habitat: Gardens and flowery places.

Flight Season: May to October.

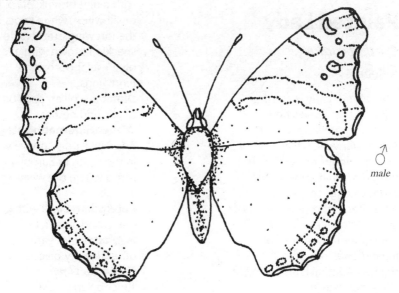

♂
male

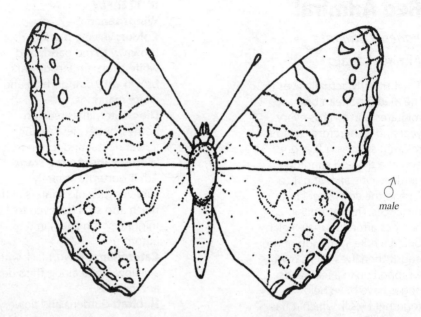

male ♂

Painted Lady

Cynthia cardui

Áilleán

The Painted Lady is another migrant that arrives here in June after growing up in North Africa. Many die because they cannot survive our winter. The butterflies that arrive in Ireland produce eggs that will hatch here later in the year. It is a fast and strong flier, which would help it get from Africa to Ireland. Like the caterpillar of the Red Admiral it also builds a shelter on leaves.

BUTTERFLY

Wingspan: 6.4 – 7.0 cm

Colour: Pale brown/orange with a hint of pink; black spots on all wings; white spots on the forewings; underside speckled brown with a row of blue 'eye' spots on the hindwings.

Diet: Caterpillar feeds on thistle and nettles.

Winter Hibernating stage: Adult (will only survive winters in the south of Europe and Africa where the weather is warmer).

Caterpillar: Black with yellow marks and spines.

Habitat: Parks, gardens and other flowery places.

Flight Season: June to September.

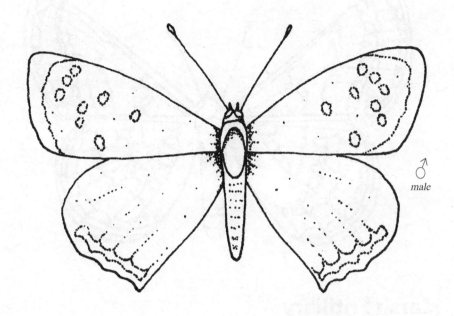

♂
male

Small Copper

Lycaena phlaeas

Copróg bheag

The male Small Copper is very territorial (does not like anything invading his territory) and so chases intruders such as other butterflies, insects and even birds away from its area. It moves quickly and easily and after an attack on an invader it will perch itself on a nearby high point ready for the next fight!

BUTTERFLY
Wingspan: 3.2 – 3.5 cm
Colour: Forewings shiny copper with dark spots and brown edges; hindwings dark brown with a copper band around the edges.
Diet: Caterpillars feed on dock and sorrel leaves.
Winter Hibernating stage: Caterpillar.
Caterpillar: Green with a dark pink stripe down its back and sides.
Habitat: Woodlands, gardens, coastal areas, heaths and meadows.
Flight Season:
May to October.

male

Marsh Fritillary

Eurodryas aurinia

Fritileán réisc

The female Marsh Fritillary is generally larger and paler than the male and its wings are a little more rounded. She lays clusters of several hundred eggs on the underside of leaves of the scabious plant. When the eggs hatch the young caterpillars stay in a group and pull a few leaves around themselves. Silk threads are then wrapped around the leaves for protection. When they are older they roll into ball when disturbed, then unroll again and quickly crawl away.

BUTTERFLY
Wingspan: 4.2 – 4.8 cm. Female larger than the male.
Colour: Pale yellowish brown with orange-brown markings and dark spots; underside pale orange brown with yellow spots.
Diet: Caterpillar feeds on devil's bit scabious.
Winter Hibernating stage: Caterpillar.
Caterpillar: Black with a grey stripe with bristles.
Habitat: Meadows, bogs, moors.
Flight Season: May to July.

Speckled Wood

Pararge aegeria

Breacfhéileacán coille

The Speckled Wood is usually found in the shadier parts of forests and woodlands where it is very territorial and will warn off other butterflies that fly into its area. As with many other butterflies the female is slightly larger than the male. She lays eggs on the blades of different types of grass and these will hatch after about 10 days.

BUTTERFLY

Wingspan: 4.6 – 5.0 cm

Colour: Dark brown with cream (northern areas) or orange-brown spots (southern areas) and many eyespots; underside speckled light and dark brown.

Diet: Caterpillar feeds on a variety of grasses and the adult butterflies feed on honeydew in trees.

Winter Hibernating stage: Caterpillar and pupa.

Caterpillar: Green with a darker green stripe down its back and lighter stripe down its side.

Habitat: Woodland clearings, gardens, paths and hedges**.**

Flight Season: April to October.

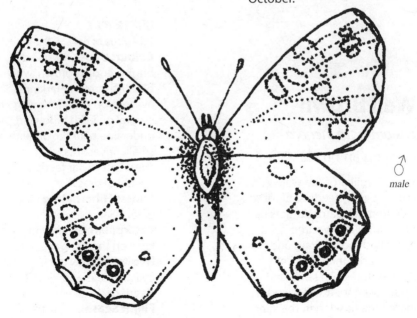

♂
male

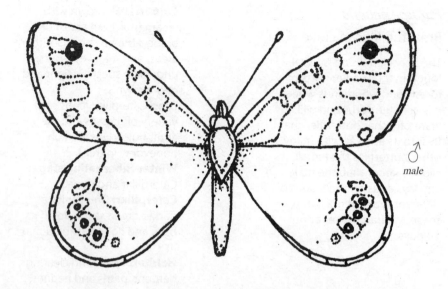

male

Wall Brown

Lasiommata megera

Donnóg an bhalla

The caterpillar of the Wall Brown usually feeds at night to hide from predators. It gets its name from its favourite habit of sunbathing on walls and stony places. It dislikes cold temperatures and so during colder weather it will spend more time basking in the sun trying to stay warm.

BUTTERFLY
Wingspan: 4.4 – 5.0 cm
Colour: Upper wings are bright reddish-brown, with blackish-brown markings; one eyespot on each forewing and several on each hindwing; underside pale brown with smaller eyespots.
Diet: Caterpillar feeds on a variety of grasses.
Winter Hibernating stage: Caterpillar.
Caterpillar: Green with white lines on the back and sides.
Habitat: Grassy areas, gardens, coastal areas and woodland clearings.
Flight Season: May to October.

Meadow Brown

Maniola jurtina

Donnóg fhéir

The single eyespot and brown/bronze colour on the Meadow Brown's forewings makes this butterfly an easy one to identify. It is a common butterfly found in a huge range of places and unlike most other butterflies, can often be seen on dull days. The female lays a single egg on a grass blade, which hatches after 2 to 4 weeks. The caterpillar usually feeds at night and spends the day low down on the stems of grass.

BUTTERFLY
Wingspan: 5.0 – 5.5 cm
Colour: Dark brown and bronze; eyespot on each forewing with a white spot in the middle; female orange-brown with a slightly larger eyespot..
Diet: Caterpillar feeds on different grasses.
Winter Hibernating stage: Caterpillar.
Caterpillar: Green with a darker line down the back and a white line along each side.
Habitat: Clearings in woodlands and forests, open grasslands, meadows, cliffs and gardens.
Flight Season: June to September.

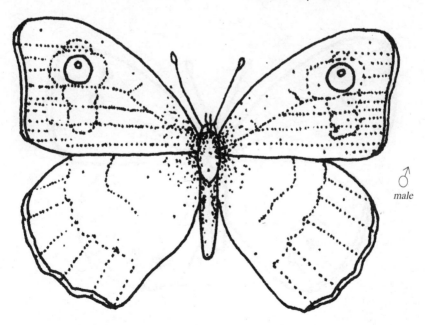

♂
male

Ringlet

Aphantopus hyperantus

Fáinneog

Like the Meadow Brown, the Ringlet can also be seen on dull days when other butterflies prefer not to fly. The female Ringlet is larger and paler than the male. She spreads her eggs over grass as she flies along. These eggs land and settle near the roots of the grass plants and hatch after about seven days. The caterpillars which emerge prefer to feed at night.

BUTTERFLY
Wingspan: 4.8 – 5.2 cm
Colour: Very dark brown with a couple of small eye-spots on each wing; underside also dark brown, with two to three eye-spots on the forewings and five on the hindwings ringed with yellow.
Diet: Caterpillar eats different grasses; butterfly feeds on nectar of bramble flowers.
Winter Hibernating stage: Caterpillar.
Caterpillar: Pale yellow with a dark band.
Habitat: Woodland clearings, meadows, damp grassy areas and hedgerows.
Flight Season: June to August.

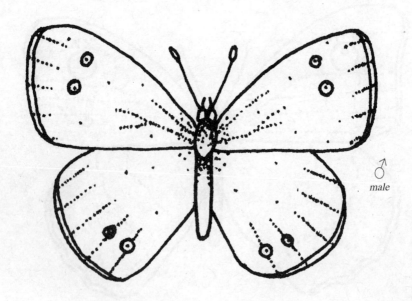

♂
male

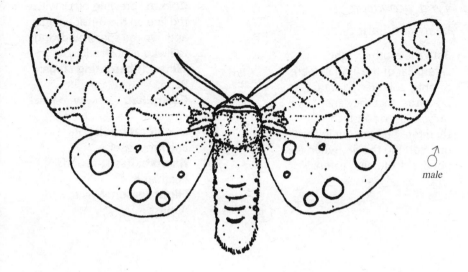

♂
male

Garden Tiger

Arctia caja

Leamhan tíograch garraí

The Garden Tiger moth varies so much in colour and markings that it is very rare to find two moths that are identical. The female is usually larger than the male.
It flies late at night and many can often be seen flying towards light. Because of its dark and hairy appearance the caterpillar is often known as 'woolly bear' and it can sometimes be seen sunbathing on warm sunny days or running along the ground.

MOTH
Wingspan: 5.6 – 7.4 cm
Colour: Forewings cream with dark brown patches; hindwings orange with black spots.
Winter Hibernating stage: Small caterpillar.
Caterpillar: Dark and very hairy.
Diet of caterpillar: Nettles, dock leaves and other garden plants.
Habitat: In gardens, meadows and other areas where its food can be found.
Flight Season: July to August.

Cinnabar Moth

Tyria jacobaeae

Leamhan flanndearg

Both the moth and the caterpillar of the Cinnabar are brightly coloured to warn predators that they are poisonous to eat. It can therefore be seen out in the open during the day when it is not at risk of being eaten.

MOTH
Wingspan: 2.4 – 4.6 cm
Colour: Forewing black with a red line on the outside edge and two red spots; hindwings red with a black edge.
Winter Hibernating stage: Pupa.
Caterpillar: Yellow with black stripes.
Diet of caterpillar: Ragwort and groundsel.
Habitat: Grassland and heathland.
Flight Season: May to early August.

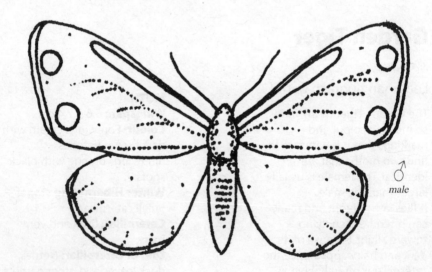

♂
male

Six-spot Burnet

Zygaena filipendulae

Buirnéad sébhallach

The adult moth and caterpillar of Six-spot Burnet can produce poisonous toxins to warn off predators. It can often be seen flying during the day. The caterpillar creates a straw-coloured cocoon on a blade of grass, inside of which it changes into a moth.

MOTH
Wingspan: 3 – 3.8 cm
Colour: Forewings black with a bluish green sheen and six red spots on each; hindwings red with black edges.
Winter Hibernating stage: Caterpillar.
Caterpillar: Pale greenish yellow with black spots and a black head.
Diet of caterpillar: Bird's-foot-trefoil (adult moth feeds on nectar of thistle and knapweed).
Habitat: Grasslands, hedgerows and meadows.
Flight Season: June to July.

♂
male

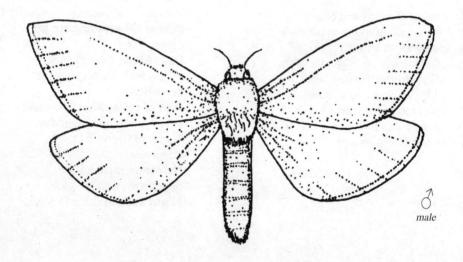

male

Ghost Moth
or Ghost Swift

Hepialus humili

Mearleamhan taibhsiúil

The Ghost Moth flies at dusk and after dark and is often drawn to light. The male moths perform a display to attract females where by they gather in groups swaying back and forth over the ground. They then give off a goat-like scent, to which the females are attracted.

MOTH
Wingspan: 4.2 – 7.0 cm
Colour: Male pale cream or silvery white; female yellowish orange. Hindwings in both male and female are grey.
Winter Hibernating stage: Caterpillar.
Caterpillar: Pale yellowish brown with dark brown spots.
Diet of caterpillar: Roots of different grasses, nettles and docks.
Habitat: Grassy areas.
Flight Season: June to August.

Emperor Moth

Saturnia pavonia

Impire

The male Emperor Moth can often be seen flying during the day looking for a female. It is sometimes mistaken for a butterfly due to its size and colourful wings. The larger female tends to come out at night, usually having spent the day resting. The cocoon in which the pupa hibernates has a ring of spines around the opening to keep away predators.

MOTH
Wingspan: 5.4 – 8.2 cm
Colour: Male has greyish-brown forewing and orange-brown hindwings; female is grey. Both have an eye spot on each wing.
Winter Hibernating stage: Pupa.
Caterpillar: Green with black bands and hairy tufts.
Diet of caterpillar: Leaves of heather, hawthorn, bramble and fruit trees.
Habitat: Woodlands, heaths and hedgerows.
Flight Season: April to May.

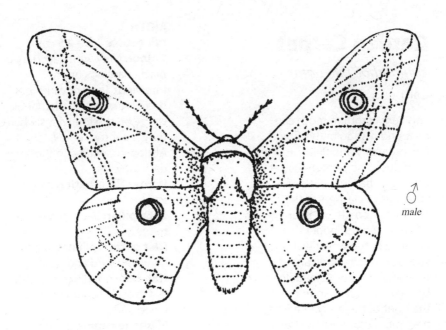

♂
male

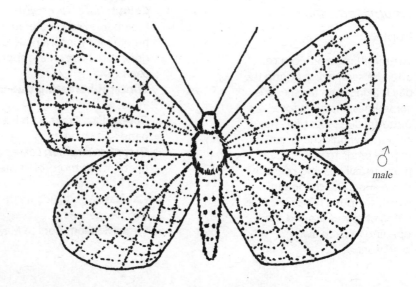

male

Garden Carpet

Xanthorhoe fluctuata

Cairpéad garraí

This very common moth can be found resting on walls and fences by day and flying about from dusk. The Garden Carpet caterpillar has two pairs of false legs or claspers at the end of its body. It has been given the name 'looper' because of the way it walks. It stretches out its body and then lifts or loops its middle to bring the claspers up to meet the front of the body. The front then moves forward to stretch out the body again.

MOTH
Wingspan: 1.8 – 2.5 cm
Colour: Grey with dark grey or black markings on the forewings. Pattern varies but there is always a dark triangle shape on the forewings where they meet the thorax. Abdomen white and thorax dark grey.
Winter Hibernating stage: Pupa.
Caterpillar: Varies from green to grey.
Diet of caterpillar: Cabbage, garlic mustard and wallflowers.
Habitat: Found in most areas but especially gardens and woodlands.
Flight Season: April to October.

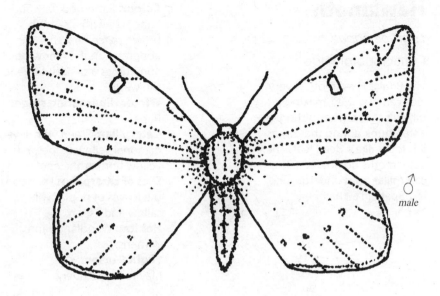

male

Brimstone

Opisthograptis luteolata

Leamhan ruibheach

Like many other moths the Brimstone flies at dusk and is often attracted to light. The caterpillar is a 'looper' like the Garden Carpet whereby it lifts or loops the middle of its body as it moves. It is approximately 30mm long and has a pointy growth on the middle of its back.

MOTH
Wingspan: 3.2 – 3.7 cm
Colour: Bright yellow with tan coloured markings; small white crescent shape, with a brown outline, on the edge of the forewings.
Winter Hibernating stage: Caterpillar (larvae) or pupa.
Caterpillar: Green or brown and looks like a twig.
Diet of caterpillar: Feeds on the leaves of hawthorn and sloe.
Habitat: Hedgerows, woodlands and gardens.
Flight Season: April to October.

Poplar Hawkmoth

Laothoe populi

Conach poibleoige

The Poplar Hawkmoth is very well camouflaged, making it difficult to see when sitting on a tree trunk during the day as it is looks like a dead leaf. The adult moths do not feed. The caterpillar goes underground to pupate in a chamber.

MOTH
Wingspan: 7.0 – 9.2 cm
Colour: Patterned dark and light grey with a reddish brown patch near the abdomen on the hindwings. Sometimes a pinkish tinge to the wings.
Winter Hibernating stage: Pupa.
Caterpillar: Green with seven diagonal yellow stripes and a yellow horn at the end.
Diet of caterpillar: Feeds on the leaves of poplar, willow, sallow and aspen.
Habitat: Woodlands and gardens.
Flight Season: May to September.

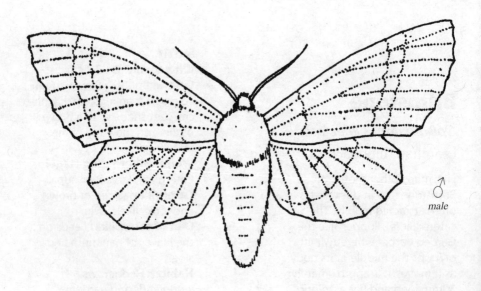

♂
male

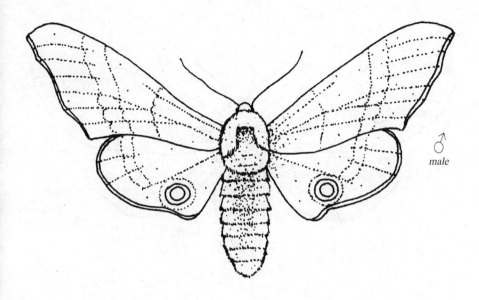

male ♂

Eyed Hawkmoth

Smerinthus ocellata

Conach súileach

The adult Eyed Hawkmoth does not feed and can often be seen sitting on tree trunks during the day. If the moth is disturbed it opens out its wings, shows the eye-spots and then rocks backwards and forwards in order to warn off predators.

MOTH
Wingspan: 7.6 – 9.0 cm
Colour: Forewings range from light brown to dark chocolate brown; hindwings pink with blue and black eye-spots.
Winter Hibernating stage: Pupa.
Caterpillar: Green with seven diagonal yellow stripes on each side and a greenish blue horn at the end.
Diet of caterpillar: Feeds on the leaves of willow, poplar and apple trees.
Habitat: Gardens, orchards and woodlands.
Flight Season: May to July.

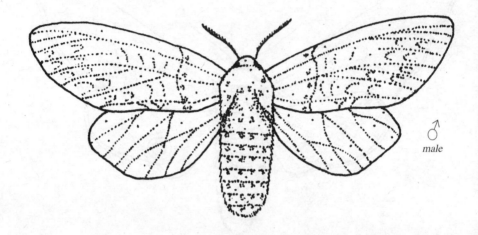

male ♂

Puss Moth

Cerura vinula

Leamhan puisíneach

The Puss Moth gets its name from its furry appearance. It is attracted to light but will land on a plant near it rather than on the light itself. Like some other moths it feeds while it is a caterpillar but not as an adult. The caterpillar is so unusual it is easy to recognise.

MOTH

Wingspan: 6 – 8 cm

Colour: White or greyish-white and furry with many black spots on the thorax and the base of the forewing.

Winter Hibernating stage: Pupa.

Caterpillar: Chubby and bright green with a black diamond shaped saddle, two long tails at the end. Head is brown, with a red collar and two black eyes on the first body segment.

Diet of caterpillar: Leaves of poplar and willow.

Habitat: Woodland and hedgerows.

Flight Season: May to July.

White Ermine

Spilosoma lubricepeda

Eirmín bán

The colour of the White Ermine's wings can vary from place to place. They are usually white but sometimes vary from creamy white to brown. Like many other moths the White Ermine doesn't feed and is also attracted to light. When it is time to hibernate the caterpillar hides amongst leaves on the ground and makes a cocoon. It is inside this cocoon that the pupa is formed.

MOTH
Wingspan: 3.0 – 4.6 cm
Colour: White with some small black spots, hairy thorax and yellow abdomen.
Winter Hibernating stage: Pupa.
Caterpillar: Dark brown and very hairy with a dark red line along its back.
Diet of caterpillar: Most low growing plants but especially nettles, dandelions and docks.
Habitat: Most habitats but especially hedgerows and gardens.
Flight Season: May to July.

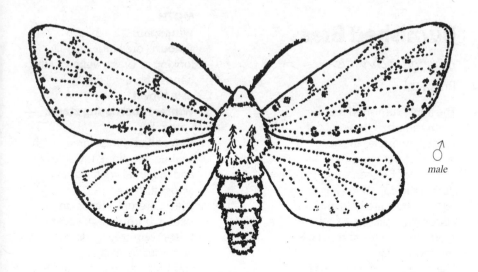

♂
male

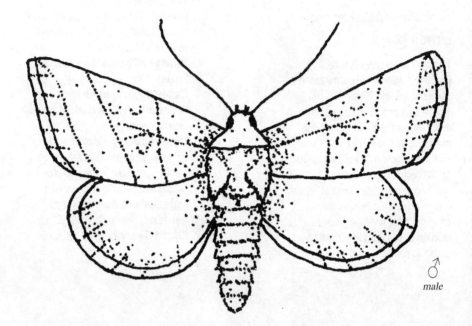

♂
male

Burnished Brass

Diachrysia chrysitis

Prásach

The adult Burnished Brass moth can often be seen feeding on honeysuckle flowers at dusk and can sometimes be seen sunbathing during the day. When it is at rest its wings are held above its abdomen, unlike most other moths who, while at rest, lay their wings flat.

The caterpillar makes a white cocoon on a plant on which it feeds and hibernates there for the winter.

MOTH

Wingspan: 3.2 – 3.8 cm

Colour: Forewings metallic looking or brassy yellow with bands of brown; hindwings pale brown.

Winter Hibernating stage: Caterpillar.

Caterpillar: Bluish-green with a white line along the sides and diagonal white stripes across its back.

Diet: Caterpillar feeds on nettles, burdock and spear thistle; butterfly feeds on honeysuckle nectar.

Habitat: Gardens, hedgerows, waste ground and meadows.

Flight Season: June to October.

Angle Shades

Phlogophora meticulosa

Scáth uilleach

The Angle Shades moth is often mistaken for a dead leaf, as the forewings are jagged and have a crumpled appearance. It can often be found resting on leaves, walls and fences during the day and near light at night. It can sometimes be seen feeding on flowers.

MOTH
Wingspan: 4.5 – 5 cm
Colour: Olive-green and pinkish-brown with a large dark triangular patch in the middle of the forewings; hindwings paler with dark lines.
Winter Hibernating stage: Caterpillar.
Caterpillar: Chubby; green or brown with a white line along its back.
Diet of caterpillar: Feeds on many plants but mostly nettles, docks and bramble.
Habitat: Gardens, hedgerows and woodlands.
Flight Season: May to October.

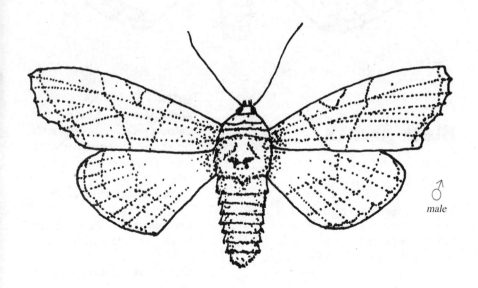

♂
male

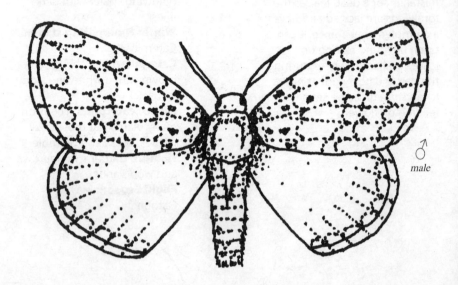

male

Black Arches

Lymantria monacha

Leamhan stuadhubh

This common moth comes out at night but can sometimes be found resting on trees during the day. The eggs, which are laid in pairs or singly, are laid under the bark. The caterpillar of the Black Arches uses the bark of these trees in which to form a cocoon.

MOTH
Wingspan: 3.6 – 5.6 cm
Colour: Forewings white with zig-zag or wavy black pattern; hindwings brown with black and white edges.
Winter Hibernating stage: Egg.
Caterpillar: Hairy and greyish-brown with black spots and lines.
Diet of caterpillar: Caterpillar feeds on leaves of pine, oak and birch.
Habitat: Woodlands.
Flight Season: July to August.